EDVARD GRIEG

PIANO CONCERTO

A minor/a-Moll/la mineur
Op. 16

Edited by/Herausgegeben von
Richard Clarke

Ernst Eulenburg Ltd

London · Mainz · Madrid · New York · Paris · Prague · Tokyo · Toronto · Zürich

CONTENTS

Ernst Eulenburg Ltd
48 Great Marlborough Street
London W1F 7BB

PREFACE

Grieg began this, the most successful of his comparatively few larger-scale works, during a vacation spent in the village of Søllerød, not far from Copenhagen, in the summer of 1868. Having graduated six years earlier from the Leipzig Conservatory, he still bore mixed feelings about his experiences there. If much of the curriculum had seemed unhelpful and pedantic, the environment of Leipzig, on the other hand, had provided invaluable opportunities for hearing as fine a range of classical and modern music as Europe could then offer. In particular, he had become a warm admirer of the instrumental and vocal works of Schumann, about whom later in life he was to contribute a laudatory article to an American journal. A more immediate testimony to his devotion exists in the form of a manuscript copy, made in his student days, of the first movement of the Schumann Piano Concerto.

A relationship between the Schumann and the Grieg concertos is plain enough. The keys are identical; the openings are alike, in each case a sequential descent of chords from the soloist, followed by a quiet statement of the principal theme (given by Schumann to the piano with woodwind, by Grieg to alternating woodwind and strings); the second subject in the relative key of C major is entrusted by both composers chiefly to the soloist; the development in both first movements is concerned for much of the time with orchestral solos accompanied by keyboard arpeggios; and in both movements the cadenza is followed by a coda in quicker tempo.

Aside from such rather superficial similarities, however, there are important differences. Grieg at the age of 25 was already too independent a character to imitate his model in slavish detail. For example, unlike Schumann he does not aim at continuity or economize in material by transforming a theme through various stages of the entire work, nor does he link the middle movement with the finale as Schumann has done with great charm. The keys of both composers' middle movements stand in third-relationship to the main tonality of A minor, but whereas Schumann chooses the lower third (F major), Grieg prefers the enharmonic upper third (D flat/C sharp major).

Grieg goes his own way in other noteworthy respects. If, from the viewpoint of constructive skill and imagination, he is far less subtle than Schumann, he exploits to a much greater extent the virtuosity of the soloist and the dramatic role of the orchestra. In this he seems to have been influenced by the example of another and a very different romantic composer, Franz Liszt, whose two piano concertos, written and revised in the 1840s and 50s, combine lyrical sentiment with technical bravura. When at work on his own concerto, Grieg could scarcely have anticipated any personal contact with Liszt, but at the end of that same year a letter arrived in Christiania from the generous old master, praising the young Norwegian's F major Sonata for violin and piano, Op.8, and expressing the hope that the composer would one day call on him in Weimar. Liszt did not of course know of the existence of the concerto, but when at last Grieg was able to see Liszt (in Rome, not Weimar, during the spring of 1870), he brought with him both the concerto and the Second Violin Sonata, Op.13. Liszt played the two works at sight, and was loud in his encouragement of their originality. It was no doubt owing to the advocacy of Liszt, and of Grieg's compatriot Johan Svendsen, that the concerto was soon accepted for publication by the Leipzig firm of E.W.Fritzsch. In the meantime, the work had been given its first public performance, during April 1869 in Copenhagen. Grieg conducted and the solo part was played by Edmund Neupert, to whom the concerto was dedicated.

The Fritzsch version probably does not represent Grieg's first thoughts on orchestration, and certainly not his later ones as standardized in the better-known scores bearing the imprint of Peters of Leipzig.[1] In the earlier version there are only two horn parts, and the score includes a tuba in addition to the three trombones. More startling, to those used to the definitive Peters editions, is the entry of the second subject of the first movement on the trumpet; whether or not this originated in a suggestion from Liszt, as is generally believed, one can only be glad that Grieg eventually decided to allot the melody to the cello section. In fact, he continued to touch up both the orchestration and the solo part almost to the end of his life. A revised edition was brought out by Peters in 1890, and in the summer of 1907, only a month or two before his death, he was working on details of expression markings and keyboard layout in collaboration with the composer-pianist Percy Grainger, who was to play the work in England at the forthcoming Leeds Festival under the composer's baton. The performance of course did not take place as planned, but in 1920 Schirmer published an annotated piano score, edited by Grainger and containing Grieg's last emendations. In the 1880s Grieg had attempted to write a second piano concerto; a few sketches remain, but in the composer's words, 'Pegasus wouldn't budge, and I gave up'.[2]

Undoubtedly much of the success of the A minor concerto on its first appearance, and of its popularity ever since, is due to the national colouring it displays. Up to the time when Grieg was writing the work, his acquaintance with Norwegian folk music must have been chiefly at second hand, though his discovery in the following year of L.M.Lindeman's monumental collection of *Mountain Melodies*[3] was a revelation. Yet he would already have caught a great deal of the spirit of traditional song and dance tunes through associating with enthusiasts like the Danes A.P.Bergreen, J.A.P.Hartmann and Niels Gade, and the Norwegians Ole Bull, Halfdan Kjerulf and above all Rikard Nordraak, who had inspired Grieg with national fervour from the time of their first meetings in 1864–5. There is even a possibility that Grieg knew something of Thomas Dyke Acland Tellefsen, the doyen of Norwegian composers living in Paris. Tellefsen's Piano Concerto, dating from 1842, introduces a folk tune into the finale. For that matter, Grieg himself had quoted a Norwegian melody in the coda of his *Autumn Overture*, Op.11.

There is no borrowed material in the Grieg concerto. Yet the whole composition is full of national idioms: the descending progression A-G sharp-E of the opening bars (sometimes called the 'Grieg' motif from its constant occurrence in his style in one form or another); the touches of modality, like the flattened seventh in the finale that moved Liszt to such excitement (solo piano, letter K, b13): the 'wavering third' of the solo horn in the second movement, bb27–8; the augmented fourths reminiscent of certain primitive scales; the rhythms of *halling* (2/4) and *springdans* (3/4, *Quasi Presto*) on which the finale is based; the free use of pedals suggestive of the drone strings of the Hardanger fiddle and the *langeleik*; the typical folk-fiddler's figuration beginning with the *animato* at D of the first movement; all weave their coloured threads into the bright tapestry.

John Horton

[1] The most important changes are listed by Gerald Abraham in: *Grieg: a Symposium* (London, 1948), 26–31
[2] Letter of 23 May 1883 to Dr Max Abraham, founder of the Leipzig firm of Peters, reprinted in: *E. Grieg: Briefe an die Verleger der Edition Peters 1866–1907*, ed. Elsa von Zschinsky-Troxler (Leipzig, 1932)
[3] L.M.Lindeman, *Aeldre og nyere norske fjeldmelodier: samlede og bearbeidede for pianoforte* (Christiania, 1853–67, ²1963)

VORWORT

Grieg begann mit der Niederschrift des erfolgreichsten seiner vergleichsweise wenigen größer angelegten Werke während eines Urlaubs im Dorf Søllerød unweit Kopenhagens im Sommer 1868. Seine Ausbildung hatte er sechs Jahre zuvor am Leipziger Konservatorium abgeschlossen, doch den Erfahrungen stand er noch immer mit gemischten Gefühlen gegenüber. Wenn auch Vieles im Studiengang wenig hilfreich und pedantisch erschien, so hatte andererseits das Umfeld in Leipzig für unschätzbare Gelegenheiten gesorgt, den hohen Standard des damaligen Europa in klassischer und zeitgenössischer Musik hören zu können. Insbesondere war er zu einem aufrichtigen Bewunderer von Schumanns Instrumental- und Vokalmusik geworden; über diesen Komponisten steuerte er in späteren Jahren einen lobenden Artikel für eine amerikanische Zeitung bei. Ein unmittelbares Zeugnis seiner Verehrung existiert in Form einer eigenhändigen Abschrift des ersten Satzes von Schumanns Klavierkonzert, die er während seiner Studienzeit angefertigt hatte.

Die Verwandtschaft zwischen den Konzerten Schumanns und Griegs ist offenkundig genug: Die Haupttonarten sind identisch; die Eröffnungstakte ähneln sich in ihrem sequenzierenden, akkordischen Abstieg des Soloinstruments, an die sich die ruhige Vorstellung des Hauptthemas anschließt (Schumann überträgt sie dem Klavier und den Holzbläsern, bei Grieg wechseln Bläser und Streicher einander ab); das zweite Thema in der parallelen Tonart C-Dur vertrauen beide Komponisten im Wesentlichen dem Solisten an; die Durchführung beider Kopfsätze beschäftigt sich über weite Strecken mit solistischen Auftritten des Orchesters über *arpeggio*-Begleitung des Tasteninstruments; und in beiden Sätzen schließt sich an die auskomponierte Kadenz eine Coda in rascherem Tempo an.

Doch neben solchen eher oberflächlichen Ähnlichkeiten gibt es bedeutende Unterschiede.

Der 25-jährige Grieg war in seiner Entwicklung bereits zu eigenständig, als dass er sich sklavisch an sein Vorbild gehalten hätte. Beispielsweise strebt Grieg im Gegensatz zu Schumann keinen inneren Zusammenhang an oder wirtschaftet sparsam mit dem musikalischen Material, indem er ein Thema durch verschiedene Stadien des gesamten Werkes umgestaltet; auch verbindet er den Mittelsatz mit dem Finale nicht, wie es Schumann so überaus reizvoll getan hat. Zwar steht bei beiden Komponisten die Tonart der Mittelsätze in Terzverwandtschaft zur Grundtonart a-Moll, doch wo Schumann die Unterterz wählt (F-Dur), gibt Grieg der enharmonisch verwechselten Oberterz den Vorzug (Des/Cis-Dur). In manch anderer bemerkenswerter Hinsicht beschreitet Grieg eigene Wege. Freilich ist er von der schöpferischen Geschicklichkeit und Phantasie her weniger kunstvoll als Schumann, doch nutzte er die Virtuosität des Soloparts und die dramatische Funktion des Orchesters weit mehr aus. In dieser Hinsicht scheint ihn ein anderer und sehr verschiedenartiger romantischer Komponist beeinflusst zu haben: Franz Liszt. Seine zwei in den 1840er und 50er Jahren komponierten und überarbeiteten Klavierkonzerte verbinden lyrische Gefühlshaltung mit technischer Bravour. Während der Arbeit an seinem eigenen Konzert konnte Grieg schwerlich einen persönlichen Kontakt mit Liszt erhofft haben; doch traf Ende desselben Jahres ein Brief des großmütigen Altmeisters in Christiania ein. Darin lobte er die F-Dur-Sonate für Violine und Klavier op. 8 des jungen Norwegers und sprach die Hoffnung aus, der Komponist werde ihn eines Tages in Weimar aufsuchen. Selbstverständlich war Liszt die Existenz des Konzerts unbekannt, doch als Grieg schließlich in der Lage war, Liszt zu treffen (im Frühling 1870 in Rom, nicht in Weimar), hatte er sowohl das Konzert als auch die zweite Violinsonate c-Moll op. 13 im Gepäck. Liszt spielte die beiden Werke vom

VI

Blatt und sparte angesichts ihrer Originalität nicht mit Worten der Ermunterung. Zweifellos ist es der Fürsprache von Liszt sowie von Griegs Landsmann Johan Svendsen zuzuschreiben, dass der Leipziger Verlag E. W. Fritzsch das Konzert bald zur Veröffentlichung annahm. Zwischenzeitlich hatte das Werk im April 1869 in Kopenhagen seine erste öffentliche Aufführung erlebt. Grieg dirigierte und den Solopart hatte Edmund Neupert übernommen, der Widmungsträger des Konzerts.

Die von Fritzsch vorgelegte Fassung gibt schwerlich Griegs ursprüngliche Vorstellungen von der Instrumentation wieder und sicherlich auch nicht die späteren, wie sie in den bekannteren Partituren von Peters in Leipzig festgelegt sind.[1] In der früheren Fassung existieren lediglich zwei Hornstimmen und in der Partitur gesellt sich den drei Posaunen eine Tuba hinzu. Überraschender für diejenigen, die mit den endgültigen Peters-Ausgaben vertraut sind, ist die Einführung des 2. Themas im I. Satz durch die Trompeten. Ob dies, wie allgemein angenommen, auf einen Vorschlag Liszts zurückgeht oder nicht: Man kann sich nur darüber freuen, dass Grieg sich letztlich entschlossen hat, die Melodie der Cellogruppe zuzuteilen. Er verbesserte in der Tat die Orchestrierung und den Solopart bis fast an sein Lebensende. Peters brachte 1890 eine überarbeitete Ausgabe heraus und im Sommer 1907, nur ein oder zwei Monate vor Griegs Tod, feilte er an Einzelheiten bei Vortragsbezeichnungen und der Anlage des Klavierparts zusammen mit dem Pianisten Percy Grainger, der das Werk in England beim bevorstehenden Leeds Festival unter der Leitung des Komponisten spielen sollte. Die Aufführung fand natürlich nicht wie geplant statt, doch veröffentlichte Schirmer 1920 einen kommentierten Klavierauszug, der von Grainger herausgegeben war und Griegs letzte Berichtigungen enthielt. In den 1880er Jahren hat Grieg den Versuch unternommen, ein zweites Klavierkonzert zu schreiben. Einige Skizzen sind erhalten, doch

wollte in des Komponisten eigenen Worten „der Pegasus [...] aber durchaus nicht mehr von der Stelle, und so habe ich es nicht fortgesetzt."[2]

Zweifellos verdankt das a-Moll-Konzert den spontanen Erfolg und seine fortdauernde Popularität zum großen Teil seinem nationalen Kolorit. Bis zur Zeit der Komposition des Werks stammte Griegs Kenntnis der norwegischen Volksmusik wohl hauptsächlich aus zweiter Hand. Indessen war es eine Offenbarung, dass er im Folgejahr die hervorragende Sammlung *Bergmelodien* (fjeldmelodier)[3] von L. M. Lindeman entdeckte. Doch wird er wohl von der Lebendigkeit der traditionellen Lied- und Tanzmelodien bereits viel in sich aufgenommen haben durch seine Verbindung mit den Dänen A. P. Berggreen, J. A. P. Hartmann und Niels Wilhelm Gade sowie den Norwegern Ole Bull, Halfdan Kjerulf und vor allem Rikard Nordraak, der Grieg von ihrem ersten Zusammentreffen 1864/65 an mit leidenschaftlichem Nationalgefühl erfüllt hatte. Möglicherweise hat Grieg sogar von Thomas Dyke Acland Tellefsen gewusst, dem Doyen der norwegischen Komponisten, der in Paris lebte. Tellefsen führte im Finale seines Klavierkonzerts von 1842 eine Volksmelodie ein. Übrigens hat Grieg selbst in der Coda seiner Ouvertüre *I høst* (*Im Herbst*) op. 11 eine norwegische Melodie zitiert.

In Griegs Konzert gibt es keine Anleihen, wenn auch die gesamte Komposition von nationalen Idiomen durchzogen ist: die absteigende Tonfolge A-Gis-E der Eröffnungstakte (das zuweilen „Grieg-Motiv" genannt wird, weil es in Griegs Stil in der einen oder anderen Form ständig wiederkehrt); der Anflug von modalen Tonarten wie die erniedrigte Sept im Finale, die Liszt so begeisterte (Klavier-Solo T. 13); die „schwankende" Terz des Solo-Horn im II. Satz T. 27f.; die übermäßigen Quarten, die an gewisse

---

[1] Die wichtigsten Änderungen listet Gerald Abraham auf in *Grieg: a Symposion*, London 1948, S. 26–31.

[2] Brief vom 23. Mai 1883 an Dr. Max Abraham, den Gründer des Leipziger Verlags Peters, nachgedruckt in *E. Grieg: Briefe an die Verleger der Edition Peters 1866–1907*, hg. von Zschinsky-Troxler, Leipzig 1932.

[3] L. M. Lindeman, *Aeldre og nyere norske fjeldmelodier: samlede og bearbeidede for pianoforte*, Christiania 1853–67, ²1963.

primitive Tonleitern erinnern; die Rhythmen von „halling" (2/4) und „springdans" (3/4, *Quasi Presto*), auf dem das Finale gründet; der freie Gebrauch der Pedale, was die brummenden Saiten von Hardanger Fiedel und Langleik andeutet; die für eine Volksmusik-Fiedel typische Figur, die mit dem *animato* bei Buchstabe D des ersten Satzes einsetzt – dies alles macht die Farbigkeit und die Leuchtkraft des Konzerts aus.

John Horton
Übersetzung: Norbert Henning

PRÉFACE

Grieg entreprit la composition de ce concerto, qui appartient au nombre relativement restreint de ses œuvres de grande envergure, au cours des vacances qu'il passa pendant l'été 1868 dans le village de Søllerød, près de Copenhague. Diplômé alors depuis six ans du Conservatoire de Leipzig, il entretenait des sentiments mêlés sur l'expérience qu'il y avait vécue. Si une grande partie de la formation lui avait parue inutile et pédante, l'environnement de Leipzig lui avait, en revanche, fourni des occasions irremplaçables d'entendre le meilleur de ce que l'Europe pouvait offrir de musique classique et contemporaine. Il était devenu, notamment, un ardent admirateur des œuvres instrumentales et vocales de Schumann, sur lequel il écrira, des années plus tard, un article laudateur pour un journal américain. Une copie manuscrite qu'il réalisa pendant ses années d'étude du premier mouvement du Concerto pour piano de Schumann constitue un témoignage très direct de son enthousiasme.

Des liens évidents unissent les concertos de Schumann et de Grieg. Les tonalités en sont les mêmes, leurs ouvertures sont identiques, à savoir une séquence descendante d'accords du soliste suivie d'une exposition paisible du thème principal (énoncé par Schumann aux piano et bois, par Grieg aux bois et cordes alternés), le deuxième thème dans la tonalité relative de *do* majeur est confié principalement au soliste par les deux compositeurs, le développement des premiers mouvements des deux œuvres consiste, en grande partie, en solos orchestraux accompagnés par des arpèges du piano et la cadence de ces deux mouvements est suivie d'une *coda* plus rapide. Cependant, à côté de ces similarités assez superficielles, d'importantes différences s'imposent. Grieg, à l'âge de vingt-cinq ans, possédait déjà une personnalité trop indépendante pour imiter son modèle servilement et dans le détail. Ainsi, contrairement à Schumann, ne recherche-t-il ni la continuité, ni l'économie

de matériel musical par la transformation d'un thème à diverses étapes de l'œuvre. Il n'enchaîna pas non plus le mouvement central au *finale* comme Schumann l'avait fait avec tant de grâce. Si les tonalités des deuxièmes mouvements des deux compositeurs respectent une relation de tierce avec la tonalité principale de *la* mineur, tandis que Schumann choisit la tierce inférieure (*fa* majeur), Grieg préféra la tierce supérieur enharmonique (*ré* bémol/*do* dièse majeur).

La personnalité de Grieg ressort dans plusieurs autres aspects remarquables. Si, du point de vue de l'habileté constructive et de l'imagination, Grieg se révèle moins subtil que Schumann, il exploite en revanche beaucoup plus largement la virtuosité du soliste et le rôle dramatique de l'orchestre, ce en quoi il semble avoir été influencé par l'exemple très différent et romantique de Franz Liszt dont les deux concertos pour piano, écrits et révisés au cours des décennies 1840 et 1850, associent lyrisme et bravoure technique. Alors qu'il travaillait à son concerto, Grieg ne pouvait prévoir qu'il entrerait en contact personnel avec Liszt. Or, à la fin de cette même année 1868, une lettre du vieux maître parvint à Christiania complimentant généreusement le jeune Norvégien de sa Sonate pour violon et piano, Op.38, et exprimant le vœu que ce dernier lui rende un jour visite à Weimar. Liszt ignorait naturellement l'existence du Concerto et quand Grieg put enfin rencontrer Liszt (à Rome, non à Weimar, au printemps 1870), il lui apporta le Concerto pour piano et la Deuxième Sonate pour violon, Op.13. Liszt déchiffra les deux œuvres dont il exhorta vivement l'originalité. L'appui de Liszt et celui du compatriote de Grieg Johan Svendsen pesèrent probablement dans la décision de la maison d'édition E.W.Fritzsch de Leipzig de publier le Concerto qui avait été créé en avril 1869, à Copenhague, sous la direction de Grieg et avec en soliste Edmund Neupert auquel il est dédié.

La version Fritzsch du Concerto pour piano ne reflète probablement pas les premières intentions de Grieg en matière d'orchestration, ni les dernières telles qu'elles sont établies dans les partitions plus connues des éditions Peters de Leipzig.[1] La première version ne comporte que deux parties de cor et la partition contient une partie de tuba en plus des trois parties de trombones. Pour ceux habitués à la version définitive de Peters, l'entrée du deuxième thème du premier mouvement à la trompette est nettement plus surprenante. Que celle-ci réponde ou pas à une suggestion de Liszt, comme on le croit généralement, on ne peut qu'être heureux du choix de Grieg de, finalement, attribuer cette mélodie au pupitre des violoncelles. En fait, Grieg ne cessa jusqu'à la fin de sa vie de corriger l'orchestration et la partie de soliste de son Concerto. Une édition révisée en parut chez Peters en 1890 et, au cours de l'été 1907, un mois ou deux avant sa mort, Grieg retravailla certains détails des indications de nuances expressives et de la disposition de la partie de clavier en collaboration avec le compositeur et pianiste Percy Grainger qui devait jouer l'œuvre en Angleterre lors du festival de Leeds suivant sous la direction du compositeur. Cette exécution n'eut bien, bien sûr, pas lieu comme prévu, mais en 1920, Schirmer publia une partie de piano annotée et éditée par Grainger contenant les dernières recommandations de Grieg. Au cours des années 1880, Grieg avait tenté de composer un deuxième concerto pour piano dont quelques ébauches subsistent mais, ainsi qu'il l'exprima lui-même, « Pégase refusait de décoller et j'ai abandonné. »[2]

Il ne fait aucun doute que le succès rencontré par le Concerto en *la* mineur lors de sa création et sa popularité non démentie depuis sont dus au coloris national dont il rayonne. Jusqu'à l'époque où il écrivit l'œuvre, la connaissance que Grieg avait de la musique traditionnelle norvégienne était surtout de seconde main, bien que sa découverte, l'année suivante, du recueil monumental de L.M. Lindeman[3], *Mélodies montagnardes*, ait été une révélation. Néanmoins, Grieg dut amplement s'imprégner de l'esprit des airs de chants et danses traditionnels par sa fréquentation des zélateurs danois A.P. Bergreen, J.A.P.Hartmann et Niels Gade, et norvégiens Ole Bull, Halfdan Kjeruf et, surtout, Rikard Nordraak qui lui communiqua sa ferveur nationale dès leurs premières rencontres en 1864/65. Il se peut également que Grieg ait connu l'œuvre de Thomas Dyke Acland Tellefsen, doyen des compositeurs norvégiens vivant à Paris, qui introduisit un air traditionnel dans le *finale* de son Concerto pour piano de 1842. Grieg, lui aussi, cita une mélodie norvégienne dans la cadence de son *Ouverture d'automne*, Op.11.

Il n'y a aucun emprunt dans le Concerto pour piano de Grieg. Toutefois, l'œuvre est riche de formules du langage musical national : progression descendante *la-sol* dièse-*mi* des premières mesures (parfois appelée le motif « Grieg » du fait de sa récurrence dans son style sous une forme ou une autre), touches de modalité telles que la septième diminuée du *finale* qui émut tant Liszt (piano solo, lettre K, mesure 13), « tierce ondulante » du cor solo dans le deuxième mouvement (mesures 27/28), quartes augmentées rappelant certaines gammes primitives, rythmes de *halling* (2/4) et de *springdans* (3/4, *Quasi presto*) sur lesquels s'appuie le *finale*, usage libre de pédales suggérant les bourdons de cordes du violon traditionnel d'Harlander et *langeleik*, ornementation typique du violon traditionnel débutant à l'*animato* du premier mouvement (lettre D), qui toutes entrecroisent leurs fils colorés dans cette tapisserie chatoyante.

John Horton
Traduction : Agnès Ausseur

[1] La liste des changements les plus importants est établie par Gerald ABRAHAM dans : *Grieg : a Symposium*, Londres, 1948, pp.26–31
[2] Lettre du 23 mai 1883 à Max Abraham, fondateur de la maison Peters de Leipzig, reproduit dans : *E. Grieg: Briefe an die Verleger der Edition Peters 1866–1907*, éd. Elsa von ZSCHINSKY-TROXLER, Leipzig, 1932
[3] L.M. LINDEMANN, *Aeldre og nyere norske fjeldmelodier: samlede og bearbeidede for pianoforte*, Christiania, 1853–1867, 2è éd. 1963

PIANO CONCERTO

Edmund Neupert gewidmet

Edvard Grieg
(1843–1907)
Op. 16

I. **Allegro molto moderato** ♩ = 84

Edited by Richard Clarke

No. 726   EE 6004

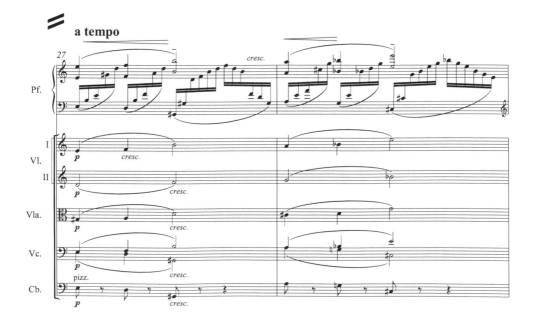

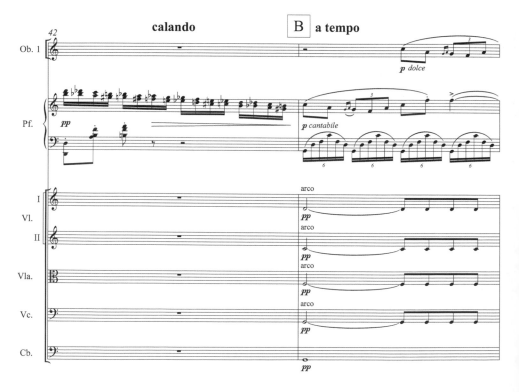

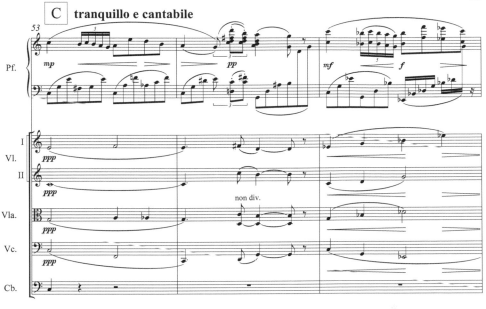

14

più animato

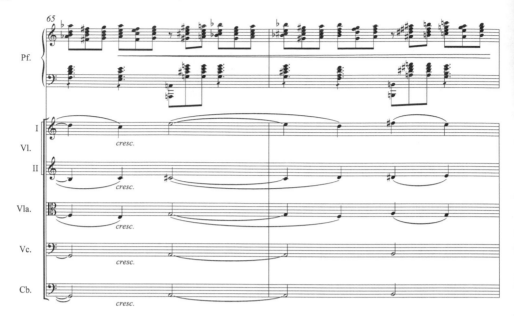

17

tranquillo ♩ = 80

22

23

poco rit.   a tempo

calando

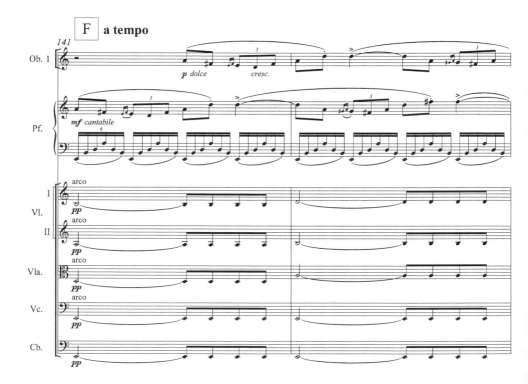

36

Tempo I

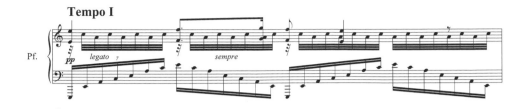

Pf.

Pf.

Pf.

Pf.

Pf.

Pf.

46

II. **Adagio** ♪ = 84

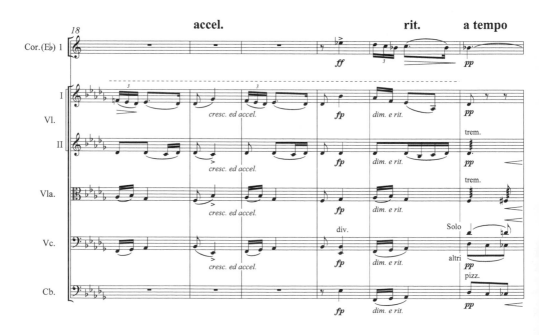

rit. A **a tempo**

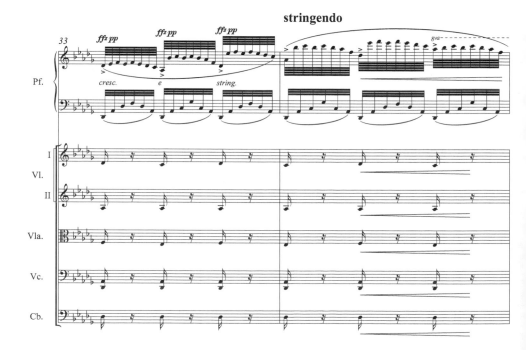

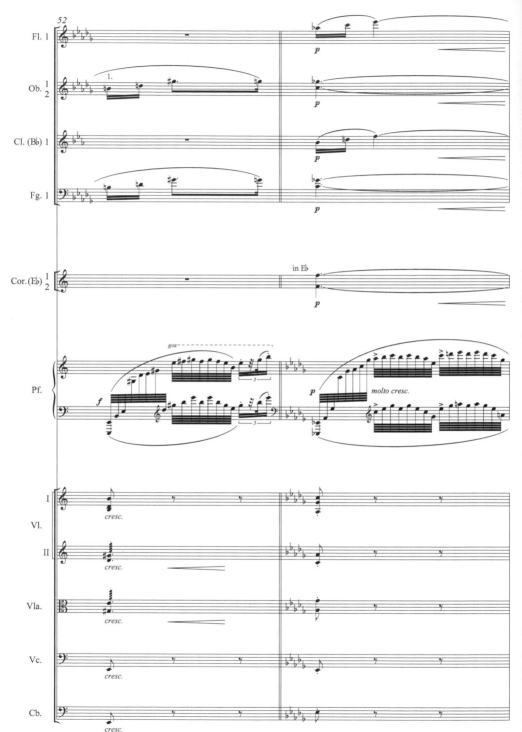

63

III. **Allegro moderato molto e marcato** ♩ = 108

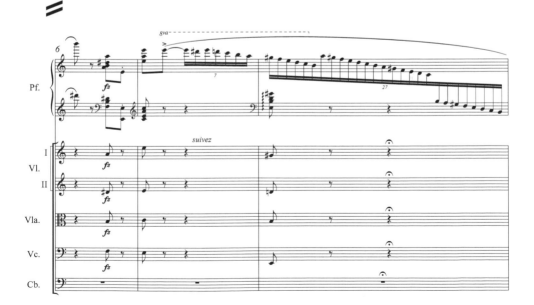

Poco animato

string.

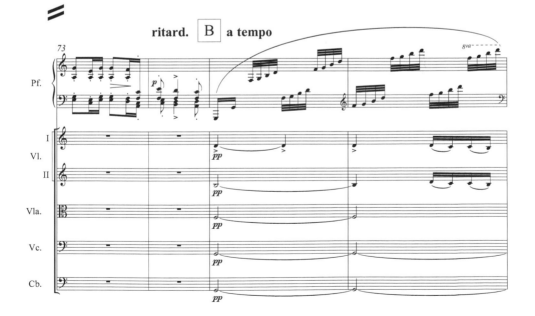

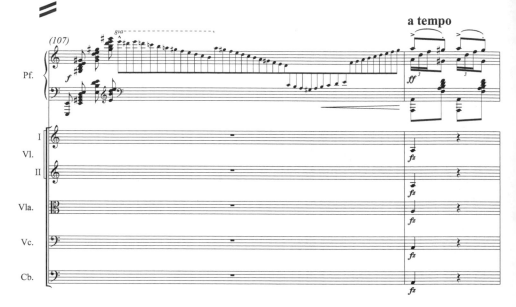

D animato

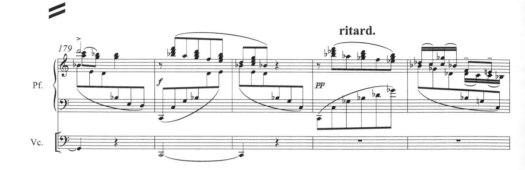

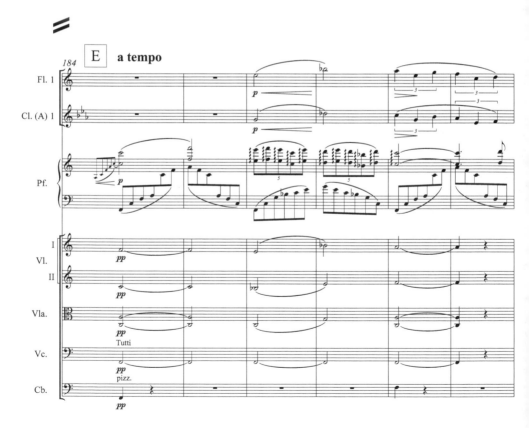

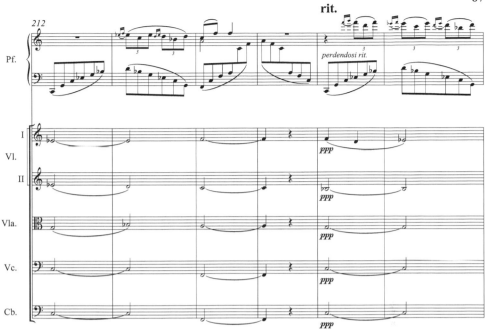

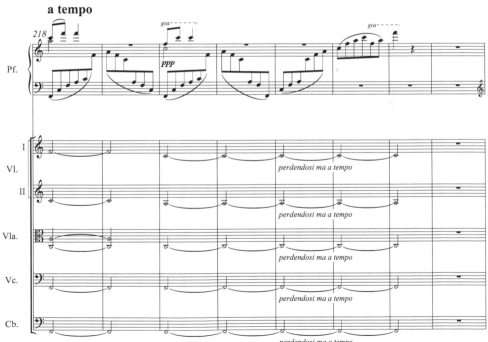

Tempo I animato

90

ritard.

Meno allegro

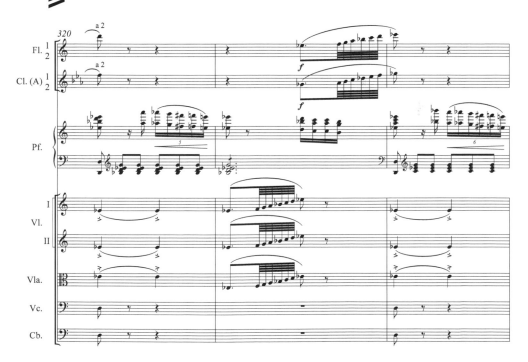

poco rit.

Flauto 2 muta in Piccolo

112

114

poco rit.   a tempo

poco rit.